Social Studies Critical Thinking

Creative Puzzles to Challenge the Brain

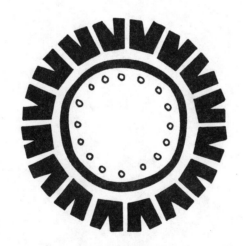

Pamela Amick Klawitter, Ed.D.

Illustrated by Bev Armstrong

The Learning Works

The
Learning
Works

Illustrations: Bev Armstrong
Editor: Linda Schwartz
Text Design: Studio E Books, Santa Barbara, CA
Cover Illustration: Rick Grayson
Cover Designer: Barbara Peterson
Project Director: Linda Schwartz

Contents

To the Teacher

Social Studies Critical Thinking gives students the opportunity to develop critical thinking and problem-solving skills. Activities can be completed by individual students, or students may challenge one another. Skills include the following:

- convergent and divergent thinking

- brainstorming

- categorizing/classifying

- visual memory

- ideational fluency

- vocabulary development

- flexibility

- force-fitting/forced association

- originality

- forecasting

- synthesizing

Okay or No Way?

Read each headline below. Find out if it really could have happened. When was the item in each headline invented or discovered, and/or when did the person(s) involved live? Decide "okay" or "no way" for each headline and prove or disprove it with the appropriate dates.

Example: Helicopter Brings Woodrow Wilson to His First Inauguration

❏ Okay: _____

☒ No way: Wilson was first inaugurated in 1913, and the first flight of a practical single-rotor helicopter was not until 1939.

1. Surviving Wright Brother Witnesses Aviation History as the Sound Barrier is Broken
   ❏ Okay: _____
   ❏ No way: _____

2. Thomas Edison Honored in White House Ceremony by President Franklin Delano Roosevelt
   ❏ Okay: _____
   ❏ No way: _____

3. X-Ray Locates Bullet in President McKinley's Stomach, But Efforts To Save Him Prove Futile
   ❏ Okay: _____
   ❏ No way: _____

4. Photocopies of President Truman's Inaugural Address Sold Across Nation
   ❏ Okay: _____
   ❏ No way: _____

5. Abraham Lincoln Honored in His Native State at the First Running of the Kentucky Derby
   ❏ Okay: _____
   ❏ No way: _____

6. Original CD Signed by Elvis Presley Sells for $4 Million at Auction
   ❏ Okay: _____
   ❏ No way: _____

7. Aqualung Aids Rescuers in Search for Survivors of the Wreck of the *Andrea Doria*
   ❏ Okay: _____
   ❏ No way: _____

Clueless

Fifteen U.S. presidents are described below—each by a two-word clue and a three-word clue. In the chart at the bottom of the page, list each president's name and the letter of both the two-and three-word clues that describe him.

2-WORD CLUES

a. Rough Rider
b. Whiskey Rebellion
c. "Black Thursday"
d. Louisiana Purchase
e. "Old Hickory"
f. Arkansas governor
g. Emancipation Proclamation
h. Navy pilot
i. Fireside chats
j. Brigadier general
k. PT-109
l. Challenger Explosion
m. Watergate break-in
n. Sputnik launched
o. Atom Bomb

3-WORD CLUES

a. Cuban missile crisis
b. Supreme Allied Commander
c. Resigned from office
d. Commander of Continental Army
e. "The Great Communicator"
f. "The buck stops here."
g. Transcontinental railroad completed
h. Declaration of Independence
i. Operation Desert Storm
j. Fort Sumter falls
k. Bull Moose party candidate
l. The Manhattan Project
m. The "kitchen cabinet"
n. Oklahoma City bombing
o. Great Depression begins

PRESIDENT'S NAME	2-WORD CLUE	3-WORD CLUE
1. _____	_____	_____
2. _____	_____	_____
3. _____	_____	_____
4. _____	_____	_____
5. _____	_____	_____
6. _____	_____	_____
7. _____	_____	_____
8. _____	_____	_____
9. _____	_____	_____
10. _____	_____	_____
11. _____	_____	_____
12. _____	_____	_____
13. _____	_____	_____
14. _____	_____	_____
15. _____	_____	_____

Herstory

Read each headline below and name the woman who is being described.

1. Former Teacher Founds Red Cross

   Who am I? _____

2. Woman Breaks Sound Barrier

   Who am I? _____

3. First Lady Rescues White House Valuables as British Advance on Washington

   Who am I? _____

4. First Woman Takes Seat on Supreme Court

   Who am I? _____

5. First Woman Nominated To Run for Vice President on Major Party Ticket

   Who am I? _____

6. First Lady Serves as Delegate to United Nations

   Who am I? _____

7. Lady Sure Shot Travels with Buffalo Bill's Wild West Show

   Who am I? _____

8. Shoshone Woman Guides Lewis and Clark Through the Pacific Northwest

   Who am I? _____

9. Her Photographs Tell the Story of the Great Depression in America

   Who am I? _____

10. Graduate Student Designs Memorial for Vietnam Veterans

    Who am I? _____

11. Former First Lady Elected to U.S. Senate

    Who am I? _____

12. First Woman Pictured on a U.S. Postage Stamp

    Who am I? _____

What a Discovery!

"Rare pairs" are two rhyming words that answer a riddle. Do research to help you figure out these rare pairs using the names (first or last) of famous inventors.

Example: Bifocals inventor's writing implements = *Ben's pens*

1. powered flight pioneers' luminary devices _____

2. telephone inventor's egg coverings _____

3. developer of the aqualung's high-level lands _____

4. sewing machine inventor's Holsteins _____

5. dynamite inventor's screams _____

6. repeating pistol developer's fasteners _____

7. steel plow inventor's bridge supports _____

8. radioactivity researcher's snowstorms _____

9. Model-T inventor's prizes _____

10. electric razor inventor's building blocks _____

11. polio vaccine developer's speeches _____

12. relativity theory developer's solar energy _____

13. mercury thermometer inventor's pencil lead _____

14. developer of psychoanalysis has a job _____

Name Game

Place names can be very interesting. Use a map of any U.S. states to find place names that fit the categories below. Challenge a friend to top your list!

List place names that are...

1. *color names:*

   Greenacres (WA, FL), Yellowstone (MT) _____

   _____

2. *edible names:*

   Tangerine (FL), Tomato (AR), _____

   _____

3. *humorous names:*

   Winkle (OH), Dink (WV), _____

   _____

4. *animal names:*

   Buffalo (NY), Boca Raton (FL), _____

   _____

5. *peoples' first names:*

   Jack (TX), Elmer (MN), _____

   _____

6. *twelve letters long or longer:*

   Pottawattamie (KS), Copperopolis (CA), _____

   _____

George, MS

CHELSEA, AL

Lynn, IN

OTIS, CO

Leslie, KY

ERIN, TN

Archie, MO

GARY, SD

Shirley, NY

KENT, DE

Tucker, WV

MONA, UT

TOM BEAN, TX

TODD, SD

Louisa, VA

SHARON, WI

Franklin, VT

HUGO, MN

John Day, OR

 # High and Dry

Read each clue below and name the mountain(s) or desert(s) being described. Answers may be used more than once.

_____ 1. mountain range that is home to both the Brooks Range and the Grand Tetons

_____ 2. Chinese desert that covers more than half a million square miles

_____ 3. highest mountain in the Western Hemisphere

_____ 4. resting place of Noah's Ark, according to the Bible

_____ 5. mountain range that is home to the wild yak

_____ 6. desert that is inhabited by the San or "Bushmen"

_____ 7. mountain range that is home to llamas, vicunas, and alpacas

_____ 8. world's largest volcano

_____ 9. mountain range where the Sherpa people live

_____ 10. highest mountain in the Alps

_____ 11. highest mountain in Africa

_____ 12. highest mountain system in the world

_____ 13. highest mountain in North America

_____ 14. world's only natural source of sodium nitrate

_____ 15. mountain range named after a Greek Titan

_____ 16. mountain chain that separates France and Spain

_____ 17. desert home of the nomadic Tuareg and Toubou tribes

_____ 18. the driest desert in the world—400 years without rain until early 1970s

_____ 19. the largest desert in the world—as large as the USA

_____ 20. low mountain range that is home to the Crazy Horse and Mt. Rushmore memorials

Battle Plan

Three events from American history are shown for each numbered problem. Place the letters of the events in the circles above the timelines in chronological order.

1. ◯ ◯ ◯
   a. Battle of Midway
   b. Battle of Verdun
   c. Tet Offensive

2. ◯ ◯ ◯
   a. Siege of Shiloh
   b. Battle of Antietam
   c. Battle of Gettysburg

3. ◯ ◯ ◯
   a. Cuban Missile Crisis
   b. Invasion of Grenada
   c. Operation Desert Storm

4. ◯ ◯ ◯
   a. Sand Creek Massacre
   b. Battle of the Little Bighorn
   c. Wounded Knee Massacre

5. ◯ ◯ ◯
   a. Boston Tea Party
   b. Battles of Lexington and Concord
   c. Boston Massacre

6. ◯ ◯ ◯
   a. Whiskey Rebellion
   b. Battle of San Juan Hill
   c. Battle of the Marne

7. ◯ ◯ ◯
   a. Burning of Washington, DC
   b. Battle of Shiloh
   c. Battle of New Orleans

8. ◯ ◯ ◯
   a. Bombardment of Fort McHenry
   b. Battle of the Alamo
   c. Trail of Tears

9. ◯ ◯ ◯
   a. Sinking of the *Lusitania*
   b. Battleship *Maine* blown up
   c. Battle between the *Monitor* and the *Merrimac*

★ ★ ★ ★ ★ ★ ★ ★ ★ ★ ★ ★

Think Fast

How many names of places <u>outside the United States</u> can you think of that will fit in each category below? Set a time limit and challenge a friend.

List place names that…

1. *are four letters long:*

   Peru, _____

   _____

2. *contain color words:*

   Yellowknife, _____

   _____

3. *begin and end with the same letter:*

   Antarctica, _____

   _____

4. *contain "rr":*

   Canberra, _____

   _____

5. *contain animal names:*

   Moscow, _____

   _____

6. *contain only one syllable:*

   Spain, _____

   _____

7. *contain the letter "z":*

   New Zealand, _____

   _____

Name _____

Who's in the News?

Name one person from American history who is being described in each of the following headlines.

1. Local Man Shocked in Kite-Flying Incident _____

2. Pilots' First Successful Airplane Flight _____

3. Fires Fatal Gunshot in Ford's Theater _____

4. Breaks Sound Barrier for First Time _____

5. First To Fly Nonstop Across Atlantic _____

6. First Human Sets Foot on Moon _____

7. Scientist Discovers Polio Vaccine _____

8. Most Decorated Hero of WWII Appears in 40 Films _____

9. Woman Founds American Red Cross _____

10. Man Designs Assembly Line to Lower Car Prices _____

11. Cotton Gin's Inventor Says It Equals 50 Workers! _____

12. One Woman Triggers Montgomery Bus Boycott _____

13. Leads Allied Forces to Victory in Gulf War _____

14. Civil Rights Leader Wins Nobel Peace Prize _____

15. Abolitionist Raids Arsenal at Harper's Ferry _____

13

American Flag Fun

Look at the flags of the U.S. states and territories. Find out what each trio of flags has in common. Find a fourth flag that fits the group. Explain what the common element is.

Example: Idaho, Alaska, Oklahoma, <u>Vermont</u>

What they have in common: **Each has a solid blue background.**

1. Louisiana, North Dakota, Illinois, _____

   What they have in common: _____

2. California, Wyoming, Michigan, _____

   What they have in common: _____

3. Idaho, Florida, Kansas, _____

   What they have in common: _____

4. Texas, Puerto Rico, Nevada, _____

   What they have in common: _____

5. Massachusetts, Alabama, District of Columbia, _____

   What they have in common: _____

6. South Carolina, Vermont, Guam, _____

   What they have in common: _____

7. Montana, Kansas, Wisconsin, _____

   What they have in common: _____

8. Iowa, Virgin Islands, Illinois, _____

   What they have in common: _____

9. Connecticut, Idaho, Louisiana, _____

   What they have in common: _____

10. Florida, Oregon, New Hampshire, _____

    What they have in common: _____

Hide and Seek

How many geographic names can you find that have each of the three-letter words below hidden inside? The three-letter word may be at the beginning, in the middle, or at the end of each word. Try to find two U.S. and two foreign names for each category.

Example:

can U.S.: <u>Can</u>ton, Cape <u>Can</u>averal, <u>Can</u>andaigua, <u>Can</u>nonsburg

Foreign: S<u>can</u>dinavia, <u>Can</u>ada, <u>Can</u>berra, Domini<u>can</u> Republic, Vati<u>can</u> City

1. **den** U.S.: _____

   Foreign: _____

2. **and** U.S.: _____

   Foreign: _____

3. **ore** U.S.: _____

   Foreign: _____

4. **tan** U.S.: _____

   Foreign: _____

5. **ash** U.S.: _____

   Foreign: _____

6. **man** U.S.: _____

   Foreign: _____

7. **ran** U.S.: _____

   Foreign: _____

8. **her** U.S.: _____

   Foreign: _____

9. **ton** U.S.: _____

   Foreign: _____

10. **ant** U.S.: _____

    Foreign: _____

Name _____

Name That State

Each headline below describes an important event related to one U.S. state. Write the year it might have appeared in a newspaper, name the state, and give a short description of the event.

1. 17th State Joins the Union   When? _____
   Where/what? _____

2. Air Force Academy Opens   When? _____
   Where/what? _____

3. Source of Mississippi River Located   When? _____
   Where/what? _____

4. World's First Artificial Heart Implanted   When? _____
   Where/what? _____

5. Hoover Dam Forms Largest Manmade Lake in U.S.   When? _____
   Where/what? _____

6. World's First Atomic Bomb Tested   When? _____
   Where/what? _____

7. Pro Football Hall of Fame Opens   When? _____
   Where/what? _____

8. World's First National Park Established   When? _____
   Where/what? _____

9. Landmark Honoring Four Presidents Completed   When? _____
   Where/what? _____

10. Father's Day First Celebrated in U.S.   When? _____
    Where/what? _____

11. First State Sales Tax Goes into Effect   When? _____
    Where/what? _____

12. World's First Hydroelectric Plant in Operation   When? _____
    Where/what? _____

13. World's Largest Chocolate Factory Established   When? _____
    Where/what? _____

Capital Con-VENN-tion

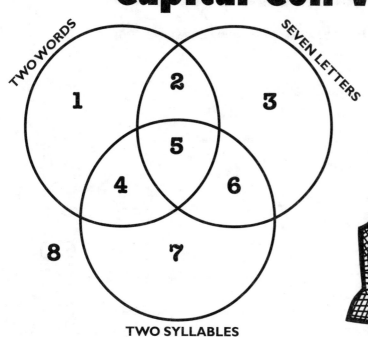

TWO WORDS · **SEVEN LETTERS**

1   2   3
5
4   6
8   7

TWO SYLLABLES

Into which of the numbered sections inside or outside the Venn diagram will each U.S. state capital's name fit? Be careful— each name can be correctly placed in only one section of the diagram, and there may be one or more sections that will not be used.

1. _____
_____
2. _____
_____
3. _____
_____
4. _____
_____
5. _____
_____
6. _____
_____
7. _____
_____
8. _____
_____

SOCIAL STUDIES CRITICAL THINKING
Copyright © 2004 The Learning Works

Presidential Rare Pairs

Each of the clues below leads to a "rare pair" of a two-word rhyming answer relating to a U.S. president.

Example: William Henry's forts = **Harrison's garrisons**

1. Eisenhower's airborne trips   _____

2. Lincoln's pig, who thought he was a sheepdog   _____

3. Washington's Grand Canyon   _____

4. Cleveland's lucky charms   _____

5. William Howard's log boats   _____

6. Herbert's U-Haul   _____

7. Gerald's squashes   _____

8. Ulysses' jeans   _____

9. Roosevelt is prepared   _____

10. Madison's fires   _____

11. a frightening Truman   _____

12. Jimmy's trade   _____

13. Clinton's feather pens   _____

14. Harding is from another country.   _____

15. Rutherford's Indian corn   _____

16. parts of eggs belonging to James K.   _____

17. Zachary's mobile home   _____

18. Eisenhower's three-wheelers   _____

19. Van Buren's cardboard boxes   _____

20. Reagan's golden arches   _____

Name _____

Flag Trios

Find out what each trio of flags has in common. Find a fourth flag that fits the group. Explain what the common element is.

Example: Yugoslavia, Netherlands, Slovakia, <u>Slovenia</u>
What they have in common: **Each has one red, one white, and one blue horizontal stripe.**

1. Japan, Bangladesh, Palau, _____

   What they have in common: _____

2. Fiji, Tuvalu, New Zealand, _____

   What they have in common: _____

3. Pakistan, Mauritania, Djibouti, _____

   What they have in common: _____

4. Albania, China, Morocco, _____

   What they have in common: _____

5. Poland, Turkey, Japan, _____

   What they have in common: _____

6. France, Liberia, Netherlands, _____

   What they have in common: _____

7. Algeria, Azerbaijan, Turkey, _____

   What they have in common: _____

8. Zambia, Uganda, Egypt, _____

   What they have in common: _____

9. Guinea, France, Romania, _____

   What they have in common: _____

10. Namibia, Uruguay, Kazakhstan, _____

    What they have in common: _____

11. China, Macedonia, Kyrgyzstan, _____

    What they have in common: _____

Women Only

Research each of the American women listed below. Write a headline that describes a major accomplishment of each woman.

1. **Pearl S. Buck** *Year born:* _____ *Birthplace:* _____

   Headline: _____

2. **Juliette Gordon Low** *Year born:* _____ *Birthplace:* _____

   Headline: _____

3. **Mary Cassatt** *Year born:* _____ *Birthplace:* _____

   Headline: _____

4. **Rachel Carson** *Year born:* _____ *Birthplace:* _____

   Headline: _____

5. **Dian Fossey** *Year born:* _____ *Birthplace:* _____

   Headline: _____

6. **Helen Keller** *Year born:* _____ *Birthplace:* _____

   Headline: _____

7. **Grandma Moses** *Year born:* _____ *Birthplace:* _____

   Headline: _____

8. **Nellie Bly** *Year born:* _____ *Birthplace:* _____

   Headline: _____

9. **Rosa Parks** *Year born:* _____ *Birthplace:* _____

   Headline: _____

10. **Amelia Earhart** *Year born:* _____ *Birthplace:* _____

   Headline: _____

Where in the World?

Unscramble each of the anagrams below to reveal the name of a country.

1. old pan   _____

2. ask paint   _____

3. neat grain   _____

4. grey man   _____

5. polar tug   _____

6. any row   _____

7. mad car saga   _____

8. I regain   _____

9. taste diet sun   _____

10. I met van   _____

11. lad in hat   _____

12. visual yoga   _____

13. oil a comb   _____

14. lantern shed   _____

15. sing opera   _____

16. can moo   _____

17. nice lad   _____

18. igloo man   _____

19. red nail   _____

20. we send   _____

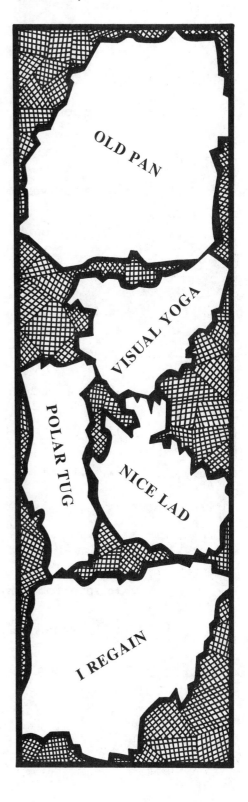

OLD PAN

VISUAL YOGA

POLAR TUG

NICE LAD

I REGAIN

21

Presidential Firsts

Name the first U.S. president to...

_____ 1. be inaugurated in Washington, D.C.

_____ 2. be born in a log cabin

_____ 3. be born a U.S. citizen

_____ 4. survive an assassination attempt

_____ 5. be born west of the Mississippi

_____ 6. resign from office

_____ 7. graduate from West Point

_____ 8. use a telephone in the White House

_____ 9. win a Nobel Prize

_____ 10. win a Pulitzer Prize

_____ 11. throw out the first pitch at a baseball game

_____ 12. die in office

_____ 13. have earned a Ph.D.

_____ 14. visit Alaska

_____ 15. appear on television

_____ 16. have oath of office administered by a woman

_____ 17. be born in the nineteenth century

_____ 18. graduate from Annapolis

State of Confusion

Use the official U.S. Postal Service abbreviations for the states to create as many words as possible in each category below. You may use proper nouns. Use the chart to find combinations of letter pairs that make words of four letters or more. How many points can you accumulate? Challenge a friend.

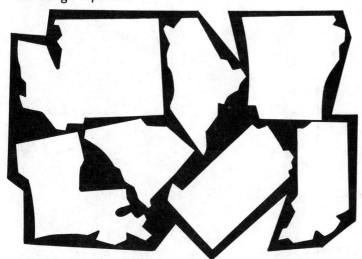

AL	HI	MA	NM	SD
AK	ID	MI	NY	TN
AZ	IL	MN	NC	TX
AR	IN	MS	ND	UT
CA	IA	MO	OH	VT
CO	KS	MT	OK	VA
CT	KY	NE	OR	WA
DE	LA	NV	PA	WV
FL	ME	NH	RI	WI
GA	MD	NJ	SC	WY

FOUR-LETTER WORDS (2 points each)

many, _____

_____

_____

_____

_____

SIX- OR EIGHT-LETTER WORDS (10 points each)

condor, _____

_____

_____

_____

_____

Capital Ideas

Name the U.S. capital that is closest to the intersection of the following latitude/longitude lines. Use a map scale to measure if necessary.

1. 120° W / 45° N

Answer: _____

2. 85° W / 30° N

Answer: _____

3. 90° W / 40° N

Answer: _____

4. 100° W / 30° N

Answer: _____

5. 115° W / 40° N

Answer: _____

6. 95° W / 40° N

Answer: _____

7. 75° W / 40° N

Answer: _____

8. 100° W / 45° N

Answer: _____

9. 110° W / 45° N

Answer: _____

10. 85° W / 40° N

Answer: _____

11. 95° W / 45° N

Answer: _____

12. 105° W / 40° N

Answer: _____

Landmark Occasions

Listed below are ten famous U.S. landmarks. For each one, write the year in which it was completed and the name of the city where it is located. Then write a newspaper headline that includes a pertinent fact about the landmark.

Example:

White House

Year: <u>1800</u> City: <u>Washington, D.C.</u>
Headline: <u>First Public Building in Nation's New Capital</u>
<u>Is Presidential Residence</u>

Washington Monument

1. Year: _____ City: _____
   Headline: _____

Liberty Bell

2. Year: _____ City: _____
   Headline: _____

Gateway Arch

3. Year: _____ City: _____
   Headline: _____

Space Needle

4. Year: _____ City: _____
   Headline: _____

Mount Rushmore

5. Year: _____ City: _____
   Headline: _____

Statue of Liberty

6. Year: _____ City: _____
   Headline: _____

Lincoln Memorial

7. Year: _____ City: _____
   Headline: _____

Independence Hall

8. Year: _____ City: _____
   Headline: _____

Alamo

9. Year: _____ City: _____
   Headline: _____

Golden Gate Bridge

10. Year: _____ City: _____
    Headline: _____

Keyography

Name _____

Use the three rows of letters from a standard computer keyboard to help you think of words for each of the following categories. Find at least two words for each category and point value. Compare your answers with a friend's.

Shaded keys score 2 points

Unshaded keys score 3 points

1. **Countries in Northern Hemisphere**

   1–10 points: _____

   11–20 points: _____

2. **U.S. States**

   1–10 points: _____

   11–20 points: _____

3. **African Countries**

   1–10 points: _____

   11–20 points: _____

4. **U.S. Cities**

   1–10 points: _____

   11–20 points: _____

5. **U.S. National Parks**

   1–10 points: _____

   11–20 points: _____

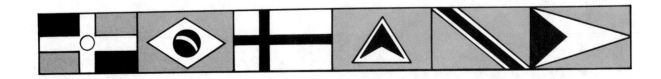

Presidential Ad-VENN-tures

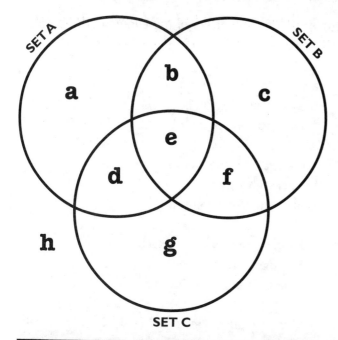

Use the information below to help you find who fits in each region of the Venn diagram. See if you can find all the names that belong in each region. Use all U.S. presidents who served during any portion of the 20th century (McKinley through Clinton). Write the names on the lines below. Hint: There may be some regions of the diagram with no names in them.

Set A: 20th-century presidents born east of the Mississippi

Set B: 20th-century presidents who served more than one term

Set C: 20th-century presidents who also served as vice president

1. Region a: _____

2. Region b: _____

3. Region c: _____

4. Region d: _____

5. Region e: _____

6. Region f: _____

7. Region g: _____

8. Region h (outside the diagram): _____

Time Flies!

Three events are shown for each numbered problem. Place the letters of the events in the circles above the timeline in chronological order.

1. ◯ ◯ ◯
   a. William McKinley born
   b. Woodrow Wilson born
   c. Theodore Roosevelt born

2. ◯ ◯ ◯
   a. Post-It© Note invented
   b. Velcro invented
   c. ballpoint pen invented

3. ◯ ◯ ◯
   a. Hudson sails into NY Harbor
   b. St. Augustine founded
   c. Ponce de Leon explores Florida coast

4. ◯ ◯ ◯
   a. *Mars Pathfinder* lands on Mars
   b. *Galileo* reaches Jupiter
   c. *Magellan* orbits and maps Venus

5. ◯ ◯ ◯
   a. John Glenn first orbits earth
   b. Yuri Gagarin first orbits earth
   c. Alan Shepard first goes into space

6. ◯ ◯ ◯
   a. first Winter Olympics held
   b. first women compete in Olympics
   c. Olympic flag first raised

7. ◯ ◯ ◯
   a. *Apollo 11* lands on moon
   b. Chuck Yeager breaks sound barrier
   c. Andy Green breaks sound barrier on land

8. ◯ ◯ ◯
   a. Levi P. Morton vice president
   b. Alben W. Barkley vice president
   c. Charles G. Dawes vice president

9. ◯ ◯ ◯
   a. Dolley first lady
   b. Mamie first lady
   c. Lady Bird first lady

Colorful Geography

Each of the following clues leads to a place name that contains a color word. See how many you can find.

Example: Mountain range in northeastern Oregon: <u>Blue Mountains</u>

1. lies between Sudan and Saudi Arabia: _____

2. capital of Yukon Territory in Canada: _____

3. oldest national park in the world: _____

4. Mount Mitchell is the tallest peak in this range: _____

5. forms much of the Texas–Oklahoma boundary: _____

6. world's largest island: _____

7. sea between Turkey and Ukraine: _____

8. prime meridian passes through here: _____

9. capital of Canada's Northwest Territories: _____

10. home of Mount Rushmore National Memorial: _____

11. early French town in Louisiana whose name means "red stick": _____

12. second-longest river in China: _____

13. Wisconsin's first permanent settlement: _____

14. main missile testing site in U.S.: _____

15. spruce-covered area in southwestern Germany: _____

16. sea between China and Korea: _____

17. central Vermont mountain range: _____

18. home range of Mt. Washington: _____

Which War?

With which American conflict is each of the items below most closely associated? Place the letter of your choice on the line in front of each item.

a. **Revolutionary War**	e. **Spanish–American War**	h. **Korean War**
b. **War of 1812**	f. **World War I**	i. **Vietnam War**
c. **Mexican War**	g. **World War II**	j. **Persian Gulf War**
d. **Civil War**		

_____ 1. agent orange

_____ 2. hawks and doves

_____ 3. Inchon landing

_____ 4. Axis versus Allies

_____ 5. *Monitor* versus *Merrimack*

_____ 6. Santa Anna

_____ 7. Pork Chop Hill

_____ 8. aircraft carriers first used

_____ 9. Emancipation Proclamation

_____ 10. Minutemen

_____ 11. Valley Forge

_____ 12. Battle of New Orleans

_____ 13. flying fortresses

_____ 14. raid at Harper's Ferry

_____ 15. Antietam

_____ 16. shot heard 'round the world

_____ 17. most American deaths

_____ 18. *Bonhomme Richard*

_____ 19. Guam and Puerto Rico become U.S. possessions

_____ 20. Rough Riders

_____ 21. invasion of Kuwait

_____ 22. started by assassin's bullet

_____ 23. amphibious landings in North Africa

_____ 24. atomic bomb used

_____ 25. sinking of the *Lusitania*

_____ 26. The Fourteen Points

_____ 27. sinking of the *Maine*

_____ 28. Bear Flag Revolt

_____ 29. Ho Chi Minh

_____ 30. Continental Army

_____ 31. Hessians

_____ 32. Nazis

_____ 33. Battle of Bunker Hill

_____ 34. Tet Offensive

_____ 35. Pentagon Papers

_____ 36. Boston Tea Party

_____ 37. MIG Alley

_____ 38. lasted eight years

_____ 39. "intolerable acts"

_____ 40. Operation Desert Storm

_____ 41. Treaty of Ghent

_____ 42. secession

_____ 43. Redcoats

_____ 44. airplanes first used

_____ 45. San Juan Hill

_____ 46. inspiration for "The Star-Spangled Banner"

_____ 47. *Uncle Tom's Cabin*

_____ 48. tanks first used

_____ 49. abolitionists

_____ 50. Cuban blockade

It's a Date!

Supply the year that each of these headlines might have appeared in a U.S. newspaper.

1959 1971 1863 1927
1849
1986
1944
1914
1886
1937
1896
1991
1920

1. New York to San Francisco Voyage Shortened by Nearly 8,000 Miles _____

2. Persian Gulf War Ends _____

3. Voting Age Lowered from 21 to 18 _____

4. Space Shuttle Challenger Explodes _____

5. Mickey Mouse Debuts in a Cartoon _____

6. Martin Luther King, Jr., Born in Atlanta _____

7. 80,000 People Rush to California in Search of Gold _____

8. Samuel Morse Sends First Telegram _____

9. Black Gold! Oil Discovered in Pennsylvania! _____

10. U.S. Teams Win 9 of 12 Events at First Modern Olympics _____

11. Statue of Liberty Dedicated _____

12. Emancipation Proclamation Promises Freedom from Slavery _____

13. Lucky Lindy Lands in Paris _____

14. Earhart Reported Lost Over Pacific _____

15. Women Get the Right To Vote _____

Alien Invasion

The aliens have landed! Identify each country they have visited by locating the intersection of the following latitude and longitude lines.

1. 50° W
   10° S

   Answer: _____

2. 100° E
   15° N

   Answer: _____

3. 5° E
   40° N

   Answer: _____

4. 30° E
   40° N

   Answer: _____

5. 170° E
   45° S

   Answer: _____

6. 30° E
   10° N

   Answer: _____

7. 45° E
   20° N

   Answer: _____

8. 75° E
   15° N

   Answer: _____

9. 105° W
   25° N

   Answer: _____

Keypad Characters

Use the numbers portion of the telephone keypad at the right to find out which of the two names in each question is worth the most points if each letter is worth the number of points on the key. Circle the name in each pair that has the higher point value.

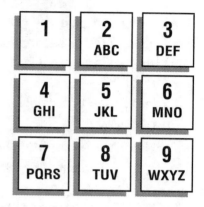

1	2 ABC	3 DEF
4 GHI	5 JKL	6 MNO
7 PQRS	8 TUV	9 WXYZ

Example: John = 5 + 6 + 4 + 6 = 21 points

1. first name of the first president . . . . last name of the 43rd president

2. Napoleon's last name . . . . Einstein's first name

3. telephone inventor's middle name . . . . Orville and Wilbur's last name

4. national anthem author's middle name . . . . Lindbergh's first name

5. Eisenhower's middle name . . . . Nixon's middle name

6. Mrs. Washington's first name . . . . Mrs. Clinton's first name

7. penicillin discoverer's last name . . . . polio vaccine inventor's last name

8. last name of first American woman in space . . . . . . .last name of first American man in space

SOCIAL STUDIES CRITICAL THINKING
Copyright © 2004 The Learning Works

I Don't Think So!

Read each headline below. Find out if it really could have happened. When was the item in each headline invented or discovered, and/or when did the person(s) involved live? Decide "okay" or "I don't think so" for each headline and prove or disprove it with the appropriate dates.

Example: Photographer Matthew Brady Captures Sinking of the Battleship Maine on Film.
❑ Okay: _____
☒ I don't think so: Matthew Brady died in 1896; the Maine was blown up in 1898, during the Spanish–American war.

1. Henry Ford Honored at First Running of the Indianapolis 500
   ❑ Okay: _____
   ❑ I don't think so: _____

2. Post-It© Notes Found in Research Lab Believed To Be Einstein's
   ❑ Okay: _____
   ❑ I don't think so: _____

3. Polartec Jacket Helps Sir Edmund Hillary Survive Cold on Mount Everest
   ❑ Okay: _____
   ❑ I don't think so: _____

4. News of Lincoln's Assassination Spreads via Telegraph
   ❑ Okay: _____
   ❑ I don't think so: _____

5. Microphone Improves Transmission of U.S. Grant's First Inaugural Address
   ❑ Okay: _____
   ❑ I don't think so: _____

6. Astronauts Enjoy Video Games Aboard First Space Shuttle
   ❑ Okay: _____
   ❑ I don't think so: _____

7. Jimmy Connors Uses New, Oversized Tennis Racquet To Win His First U.S. Open
   ❑ Okay: _____
   ❑ I don't think so: _____

It's a Wonder!

Find out about the Seven Wonders of the Ancient World, and name those that match each of the descriptions below.

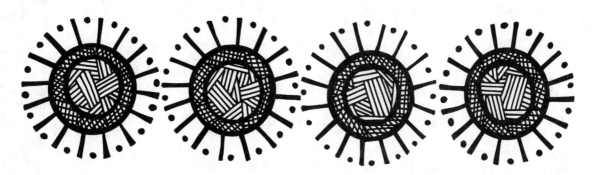

1. stood on the island of Pharos in Egypt   _____

2. about as high as the Statue of Liberty   _____

3. holds remains of Persian ruler   _____

4. stood in the Greek city of Ephesus   _____

5. built as tombs for Egyptian kings   _____

6. built by Greek sculptor Phidias   _____

7. stood on an island in the Aegean Sea   _____

8. believed to have been built by King Nebuchadnezzar II   _____

9. honored the sun god, Helios   _____

10. believed to have been toppled by an earthquake   _____

11. near modern-day Baghdad, Iraq   _____

12. fire burned near top to provide light   _____

13. designed by Greek architects Satyros and Pythios   _____

14. honors the Greek goddess of hunting and wild animals   _____

15. probably topped with a sculpture of a chariot   _____

16. the only one(s) remaining today   _____

17. designed by the Greek architect Sostratos   _____

18. fashioned of gold and ivory   _____

Monumental Discoveries

Name the ancient monument that is being described in each of the following headlines.

1. Life-Size Army of Soldiers Discovered in Chinese Tomb

   What? _____

2. Huge Carved Stone Heads Represent Early American Culture

   What? _____

3. Ancient Temple Probably Best Example of Greek Architecture

   What? _____

4. More Than 600 Carved Stone Statues Scattered Across South Pacific Island

   What? _____

5. Man Or Lion? Egyptian Desert Home to Giant Limestone Monument

   What? _____

6. Gigantic Bronze Statue Believed to Have Guarded Harbor on Aegean Island

   What? _____

7. Half-Ruined Amphitheater Still One of Chief Roman Landmarks

   What? _____

8. Southwestern England Boasts Ancient Circular Stone Tribal Gathering Place

   What? _____

9. 100-Foot Carved Column Honors Roman Emperor After Conquest of Dacia

   What? _____

10. Hiram Bingham Discovers Stone Ruins of Ancient City on Andean Mountainside

    What? _____

Let's Get Civilized

Match each item in the list below to the civilization with which it is most closely associated. Write each item in its correct column.

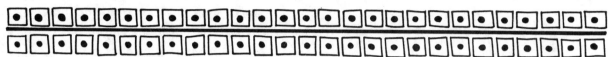

Osiris	Icarus	drachma	Trojan War
catapult	Hadrian's Wall	Acropolis	potter's wheel
senate	Sparta	pharaohs	Colosseum
arched bridges	fasces	Pompeii	papyrus boats
Thebes	Homer	public baths	Sphinx
aqueduct	Lion Gate	toga	Forum
Olympics	senet	legionnaire	signs of zodiac
cat mummies	Rosetta stone	ankh	gladiators
triremes	hieroglyphics	Ionic Order	Socrates

Ancient Egypt	Ancient Greece	Ancient Rome
_____	_____	_____
_____	_____	_____
_____	_____	_____
_____	_____	_____
_____	_____	_____
_____	_____	_____
_____	_____	_____
_____	_____	_____
_____	_____	_____
_____	_____	_____
_____	_____	_____
_____	_____	_____
_____	_____	_____

Architectural Ad-VENN-tures

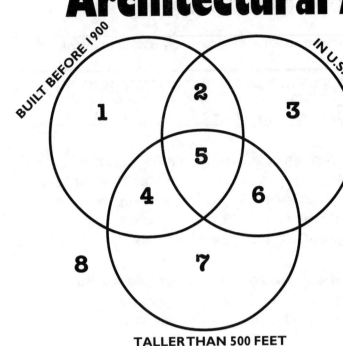

BUILT BEFORE 1900

IN U.S.A.

1   2   3

5

4   6

8   7

TALLER THAN 500 FEET

Do research on the famous buildings listed below. Place the name of each building on the numbered line matching the section in (or outside) the Venn diagram where it belongs. Be careful—each name can be correctly placed in only one section!

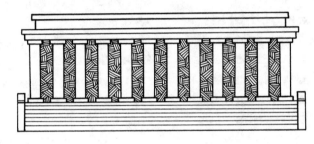

Eiffel Tower

Statue of Liberty

Gateway Arch

Sydney Opera House

Space Needle

Leaning Tower of Pisa

Washington Monument

Petronas Towers

Lincoln Memorial

Sears Tower

White House

Taj Mahal

U.S. Capitol

Colosseum

1. _____
_____
_____
2. _____
_____
_____
3. _____
4. _____
5. _____
6. _____
_____
_____
7. _____
8. _____

Presidential Newsmakers

Name the president(s) described in each of the following headlines.

_____ 1. Governor of Georgia Moves Into White House

_____ 2. President Gets Stuck in Bathtub

_____ 3. President Attends Rough Riders Reunion

_____ 4. Former President Tries Skydiving

_____ 5. President Sworn In By His Own Father

_____ 6. A President's Grandson Marries a President's Daughter

_____ 7. Second Presidential Assassination Stuns Nation

_____ 8. Nation Saddened By Deaths of Two Former Presidents Today

_____ 9. President Takes Oath of Office on Airplane

_____ 10. Rhodes Scholar Becomes President

_____ 11. President Married in White House

_____ 12. Grandson of Former President Takes Office

_____ 13. Last of the Whigs Leaves Office

_____ 14. President Founds League of Nations

_____ 15. President Gives Go-Ahead To Drop Atom Bomb

Capital Anagrams

Unscramble each of the anagrams below to reveal the name of a U.S. capital city.

1. smart ocean _____

2. iron temple _____

3. icy cartons _____

4. a shell at sea _____

5. fling spider _____

6. lad is in piano _____

7. dove prince _____

8. joy first fence _____

9. oily map _____

10. shrug briar _____

11. I need moss _____

12. short clean _____

13. eat all sticky _____

14. back rims _____

15. safe tan _____

16. pet oak _____

17. calamity hook _____

18. spoil Anna _____

19. one tour bag _____

20. not more gym _____

D.C. Landmarks

Write the name of the Washington, D.C. landmark described in each headline.

1. Lindbergh's *Spirit of St. Louis* Finds a New Home

   Landmark: _____

2. Original Copy of Declaration of Independence on Display

   Landmark: _____

3. Pierre L'Enfant, Designer of Washington, D.C., Buried Here

   Landmark: _____

4. Black Granite Wall Holds the Names of 58,000 Missing and Dead

   Landmark: _____

5. 193 Carved Memorial Stones Part of Completed Monument

   Landmark: _____

6. John Russell Pope Designs Shrine to Third President

   Landmark: _____

7. Site of Lincoln's Assassination

   Landmark: _____

8. Statue of Freedom Sits Atop Popular Landmark

   Landmark: _____

9. Bronze Statue Remembers WWII Accomplishments of U.S. Marines

   Landmark: _____

10. Billions of Bills and Postage Stamps Produced Here Each Year

    Landmark: _____

Who Said So?

Who is famous for each of the quotes below? Choose speakers from among the following:

Benjamin Franklin	**Mark Twain**	**John F. Kennedy**	**Martin Luther King, Jr.**
Emma Lazarus	**Patrick Henry**	**Francis Scott Key**	**Abraham Lincoln**
Neil Armstrong	**Thomas Jefferson**	**Nathan Hale**	**Franklin D. Roosevelt**

Select three of these quotes. On the back of your paper, tell the significance of each quote.

1. "I only regret that I have but one life to lose for my country."
   Who/what? _____

2. "I know not what course others may take; but as for me, give me liberty, or give me death."
   Who/what? _____

3. "Early to bed and early to rise, makes a man healthy, wealthy, and wise."
   Who/what? _____

4. "Ask not what your country can do for you—ask what you can do for your country."
   Who/what? _____

5. "I have a dream that my four little children will one day live in a nation where they will not be
   judged by the color of their skin, but by the content of their character."
   Who/what? _____

6. "That's one small step for a man, one giant leap for mankind."
   Who/what? _____

7. "We would rather die on our feet than live on our knees."
   Who/what? _____

8. "The land of the free and the home of the brave."
   Who/what? _____

9. "…government of the people, by the people, for the people, shall not perish from the earth."
   Who/what? _____

10. "We hold these truths to be self-evident, that all men are created equal."
    Who/what? _____

A Rainbow of Facts

Each of the following clues leads to a word or phrase that contains a color word. See how many you can find.

Example: Mountain range in northeastern Oregon: Blue Mountains

_____ 1. Great Plains Indian tribe

_____ 2. 1600 Pennsylvania Avenue

_____ 3. Paul Revere was one

_____ 4. Clara Barton founded this organization

_____ 5. medal awarded to members of U.S. armed forces wounded in action

_____ 6. 1849 had a famous one

_____ 7. abolitionist who raided Harper's Ferry, Virginia

_____ 8. Alabama's state bird

_____ 9. state flower of Texas

_____ 10. spans the entrance to San Francisco Bay

_____ 11. Ethan Allen was their leader

_____ 12. first professional U.S. baseball team

_____ 13. famous British pirate

_____ 14. British soldiers during Revolutionary War

_____ 15. gradual warming of the earth's surface

_____ 16. February observance to honor African-Americans

_____ 17. California's nickname

_____ 18. Colorado's state tree

SOCIAL STUDIES CRITICAL THINKING
Copyright © 2004 The Learning Works

More Keyography

Use the three rows of letters from a standard computer keyboard to help you think of at least two words in each of the following categories. Compare your answers with a friend's.

Shaded keys are typed with the left hand.

Unhaded keys are typed with the right hand.

1. Major U.S. Cities

fewer than 8 letters and fewer than 3 right-hand keys: _____ _____

more than 8 letters and more than 3 right-hand keys: _____ _____

2. Countries in Asia

fewer than 8 letters and fewer than 3 right-hand keys: _____ _____

more than 8 letters and more than 3 right-hand keys: _____ _____

3. Countries in Europe

fewer than 8 letters and fewer than 3 right-hand keys: _____ _____

more than 8 letters and more than 3 right-hand keys: _____ _____

4. Major European Cities

fewer than 8 letters and fewer than 3 right-hand keys: _____ _____

more than 8 letters and more than 3 right-hand keys: _____ _____

5. Major Islands

fewer than 8 letters and fewer than 3 right-hand keys: _____ _____

more than 8 letters and more than 3 right-hand keys: _____ _____

That's Silly!

Use a road map or atlas to help search out twenty comical town names in your state. Make a list in the space below. Then, choose one of the two follow-up writing options.

State: _____

1. _____   11. _____
2. _____   12. _____
3. _____   13. _____
4. _____   14. _____
5. _____   15. _____
6. _____   16. _____
7. _____   17. _____
8. _____   18. _____
9. _____   19. _____
10. _____   20. _____

• Write a fictional account of how one of these towns got its name.
   or
• Write a humorous paragraph that includes at least 10 of these names.

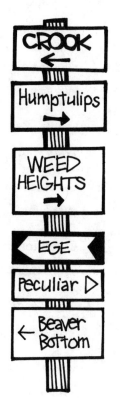

_____

_____

_____

_____

_____

_____

_____

_____

Name _____

Historic Headlines

Each headline below describes an important event in U.S. history. Write the year it might have appeared in a newspaper and give a short description of the event.

1. First Edition of *Poor Richard's Almanack* Published   Year: _____
   Who/what? _____

2. Army Officers Lead Expedition from Mississippi River to Pacific Ocean   Year: _____
   Who/what? _____

3. Former Slave Killed in Colonial Rebellion   Year: _____
   Who/what? _____

4. Wilderness Road Opened Into Kentucky   Year: _____
   Who/what? _____

5. Religious Group Arrives with Plans to Transform Utah's Desert   Year: _____
   Who/what? _____

6. For First Time, Mail Reaches California in Only 10 Days   Year: _____
   Who/what? _____

7. English Ship Returns To Discover Colony Has Disappeared   Year: _____
   Who/what? _____

8. Pilgrims Sign Agreement Before Disembarking   Year: _____
   Who/what? _____

9. Lawyer Pens Poem as Fort McHenry Is Bombarded   Year: _____
   Who/what? _____

10. East Meets West at Promontory Point   Year: _____
    Who/what? _____

11. Outnumbered Texans Refuse To Surrender: All Killed   Year: _____
    Who/what? _____

12. Confederate Troops Surrender at Appomattox   Year: _____
    Who/what? _____

13. National Waterway Completed Across State of New York   Year: _____
    Who/what? _____

Next-Door Neighbors

For this activity, find geographic names that contain "side by side" letters (adjacent letters in alphabetical order). Think of names to fit each category below. Score two points for every name you can come up with. Set a time limit and challenge a friend.

1. cities that begin with side-by-side letters:

   Abilene, _____

   _____

2. cities that have side-by-side letters inside:

   Constantinople, _____

   _____

3. countries that begin with side-by-side letters:

   Turkey, _____

   _____

4. countries that have side-by-side letters inside:

   Chile, _____

   _____

5. land features (mountains, deserts, etc.) that have side-by-side letters:

   Himalaya, _____

   _____

6. bodies of water that begin with side-by-side letters:

   Klondike River, _____

   _____

More Fun with Place Names

Use any state map to find towns and cities to fit each category below. Challenge a friend!

1. weather-related names:

   Hurricane, WV; Risingsun, OH; _____

   _____

2. four-letter names:

   Rice, NM; Clem, KY; _____

   _____

3. foreign-sounding cities:

   Scotland, PA; Poland, IN; _____

   _____

4. cities that sound like states:

   Ohio, IL; Kansas, GA; _____

   _____

5. names with numbers:

   Hundred, WV; Eightyfour, PA; _____

   _____

6. physical feature names:

   Canyon, TX; Cliff, KY; _____

   _____

Baseball Greats Rare Pairs

Each of the clues below leads to a "rare pair" (rhyming two-word phrase) relating to a famous professional baseball player.

1. McGwire's flickers of fire _____

2. Mantle is cagey _____

3. Williams's bagels _____

4. Dimaggio's troubles _____

5. Cobb's astonishment _____

6. Berra's sandwiches _____

7. Boggs's garden tools _____

8. Rose's accomplishments _____

9. Musial's schemes _____

10. Babe's principles _____

11. Griffey's chickens _____

12. Bonds's songbirds _____

13. Mays's soups _____

14. Garvey's arm coverings _____

15. Ripken's friends _____

16. Sosa's magic spells _____

17. Campanella's loud sounds _____

18. Aaron's boards _____

19. Koufax's fudge _____

20. Whitey's prize _____

Liquid Logic

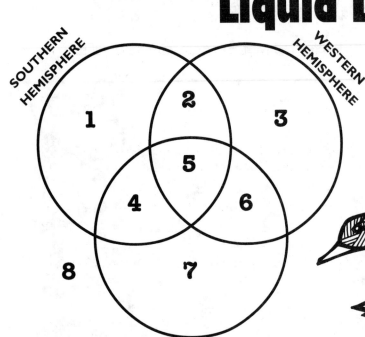

SOUTHERN HEMISPHERE

WESTERN HEMISPHERE

1   2   3

5

4   6

8   7

AREA GREATER THAN 20,000 SQUARE MILES

Do research on the bodies of water listed below. Place the name of each one on the numbered line matching the section in (or outside) the Venn diagram where it belongs. Be careful—each name can be correctly placed in only one section!

Caribbean Sea

Baltic Sea

Lake Victoria

Lake Nipigon

Lake Rudolph

Reindeer Lake

Lake Tanganyika

Hudson Bay

Bay of Bengal

Bering Sea

Lake Winnipeg

Aral Sea

Caspian Sea

Weddell Sea

Lake Titicaca

Red Sea

1. _____

2. _____

3. _____

_____

_____

_____

4. _____

5. _____

6. _____

_____

_____

7. _____

_____

_____

8. _____

River Riddles

Each of the descriptions below gives clues about a famous river somewhere in the world. Name each river.

_____ 1. forms part of the boundary between the U.S. and Mexico

_____ 2. the longest river that is entirely within England and flows through the center of London

_____ 3. plunges over Victoria Falls and is the fourth longest river in Africa

_____ 4. Europe's longest river, most of its length is frozen for three months of the year

_____ 5. its longest branch is the Platte River, and it drains the area that Lewis and Clark explored

_____ 6. flows past Mt. Vernon and Harpers Ferry, and forms the boundary between Maryland, West Virginia, and Virginia

_____ 7. begins in an ice cave in the Himalaya and is considered sacred by Hindus—their temples line its banks

_____ 8. its beauty inspired Johann Strauss to write a famous waltz

_____ 9. the river mentioned most often in the Bible

_____ 10. forms the boundary between New York and Pennsylvania; a famous painting shows George Washington crossing

_____ 11. the longest river in Canada, named for a Canadian explorer

_____ 12. connects Lake Erie to Lake Ontario, and is the site of a spectacular waterfall and one of the world's largest hydroelectric plants

_____ 13. its floodwaters are controlled by the Aswan Dam

_____ 14. links the Great Lakes to the Atlantic Ocean

_____ 15. flows through the heart of Paris where it is spanned by more than thirty bridges

51

That's Not Natural!

Each headline below tells about a famous building or other manmade structure.
Give the name of the structure, and tell where it can be found.

1. Unstable Soil Causes Tower To Lean

   Name: _____   *Location:* _____

2. Indian Ruler Orders White Marble Tomb Built in Memory of Favorite Wife

   Name: _____   *Location:* _____

3. Parliament names Bell in Clock Tower After Commissioner of Works

   Name: _____   *Location:* _____

4. Landmark Fortress Was Center of Soviet Union's Government Until 1991

   Name: _____   *Location:* _____

5. U.S. Spends $8 Billion To Transport Arctic Oil 800 Miles

   Name: _____   *Location:* _____

6. Landowski Sculpture Watches Over Brazilian City from Atop Corcovado Mountain

   Name: _____   *Location:* _____

7. Passenger and Freight Trains Travel Beneath the Atlantic to Link France and the U.K.

   Name: _____   *Location:* _____

8. Waterfront Arts Center is World's Busiest—Nearly 1,000 Rooms Beneath Sail-Like Roof

   Name: _____   *Location:* _____

9. Royal Residence built by King Louis XIV Is Now a French National Museum

   Name: _____   *Location:* _____

10. World's Largest Artificially Created Waterway System Is Over 1,000 Miles Long

    Name: _____   *Location:* _____

11. Magnificent Moorish Palace Now a Spanish Monument

    Name: _____   *Location:* _____

12. Virginia Estate of First President Now a National Shrine

    Name: _____   *Location:* _____

Decade Dilemma

Place the letter of each event below in the column showing the decade in which it happened.

a. Korean War begins
b. Yuri Gagarin is the first man in space
c. John F. Kennedy is assassinated
d. ENIAC, the first electronic computer, is built
e. Rosa Parks refuses to sit at the back of the bus
f. Chuck Yeager breaks the sound barrier
g. Japan launches a surprise attack on Pearl Harbor
h. first human heart transplant is performed
i. first atomic submarine is launched
j. Alaska and Hawaii become states
k. first meeting of the United Nations General Assembly
l. Sputnik is launched, beginning the Space Age
m. the Pentagon is completed, becoming the largest office building in the world
n. Martin Luther King, Jr., gives his "I Have a Dream" speech
o. Woodstock music festival takes place
p. the Manhattan Project is begun
q. Edmund Hillary and Tenzing Norgay reach the summit of Mt. Everest
r. Neil Armstrong is the first to set foot on the moon
s. the Beatles appear on "The Ed Sullivan Show"
t. Jonas Salk invents polio vaccine
u. *Brown versus Board of Education* bans racial segregation in public schools

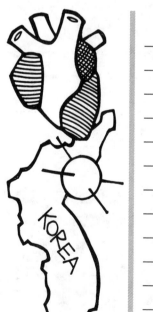

1940s	1950s	1960s
_____	_____	_____
_____	_____	_____
_____	_____	_____
_____	_____	_____
_____	_____	_____
_____	_____	_____
_____	_____	_____
_____	_____	_____
_____	_____	_____

Early Americans

With which early civilization(s) is each of the following places or things most closely associated?
Place the following letter(s) next to the appropriate items below:

A: Aztec B: Inca C: Maya D: Anasazi E: Olmec

_____ 1. last ruler was Atahualpa

_____ 2. black-on-white painted pottery

_____ 3. Quetzalcoatl

_____ 4. Mesa Verde

_____ 5. Pizarro

_____ 6. La Venta

_____ 7. had ceremonial chambers called "kivas"

_____ 8. mountains of Peru

_____ 9. built pyramids

_____ 10. buried their dead under the floors of the houses in which they lived

_____ 11. practiced trephining

_____ 12. Lake Texcoco

_____ 13. cliff dwellers

_____ 14. inhabited the Four Corners region

_____ 15. Pachacuti

_____ 16. ancestors of modern Pueblo peoples

_____ 17. Quechua language

_____ 18. conquered by Cortes

_____ 19. large stone carvings of heads

_____ 20. Montezuma

_____ 21. Chaco Canyon

_____ 22. farmed on floating islands

_____ 23. made advances in astronomy

_____ 24. flourished 1200 to 400 B.C.

_____ 25. Tenochtitlan was their capital

_____ 26. Macchu Picchu

_____ 27. math system based on 20

_____ 28. name means "Ancient Ones"

_____ 29. Temple of the Sun

_____ 30. made books of fig tree bark

_____ 31. calendar stone sculpture survived

_____ 32. occupied Mexico

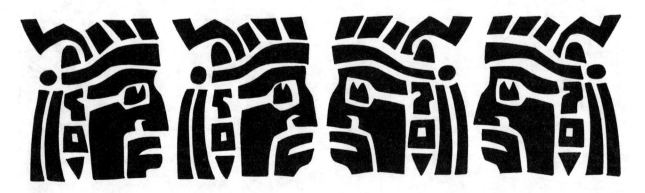

Continental Geography

On which continent is each of the following located? Place the number of each item in the correct column at the bottom of the page.

1. Great Barrier Reef
2. Great Rift Valley
3. Gulf of Tonkin
4. Victoria Island
5. Atlas Mountains
6. Ayers' Rock
7. Victoria Falls
8. Bay of Bengal
9. Sierra Nevada Mtns.
10. Cape of Good Hope
11. Great Sandy Desert
12. Cape Horn
13. Jutland Peninsula
14. Patagonia
15. Bass Strait
16. Baffin Bay
17. Apennine Peninsula
18. Atacama Desert
19. Lapland
20. Gulf of Carpentaria
21. Angel Falls
22. Bay of Fundy
23. Mount Fuji
24. Paricutin Volcano

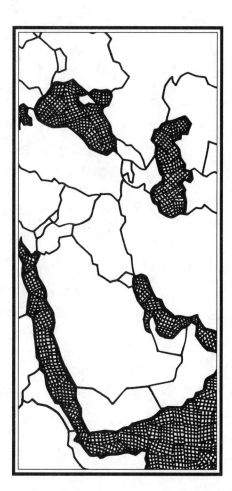

25. Strait of Magellan
26. Sea of Okhotsk
27. Labrador Sea
28. Giants' Causeway
29. Arafura Sea
30. Kamchatka Peninsula
31. Gulf of Oman
32. Kalahari Desert
33. Pyrenees
34. Timbuktu
35. Lake Titicaca
36. Great Dividing Range
37. Mammoth-Flint Caves
38. Dead Sea
39. Mount Olympus
40. Kilimanjaro
41. Carpathian Mountains
42. Rock of Gibraltar
43. Mount Kosciusko
44. Falkland Islands
45. Annapurna
46. Horseshoe Falls
47. Siberia
48. Great Victoria Desert

Africa	Asia	Australia	Europe	N. America	S. America

What a Disaster!

Three disasters are shown for each numbered problem. Place the letters of the events in the circles above the timeline in chronological order.

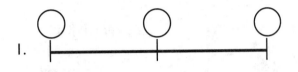

1.

a. hurricane kills more than 6,000 in Galveston, Texas
b. Spanish influenza kills 500,000 Americans
c. 500 dead or missing after San Francisco earthquake

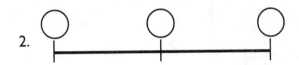

2.

a. *Exxon Valdez* oil spill in Alaska
b. steamboat *Sultana* explodes on Mississippi river
c. Johnstown, Pennsylvania, flood kills more than 2,200

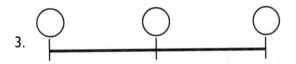

3.

a. coal mine explosion in Monongah, West Virginia, kills 361
b. *Titanic* sinks, killing more than 1,500
c. earthquake in Peru kills more than 50,000

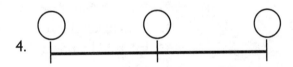

4.

a. cargo vessel *Edmund Fitzgerald* sinks
b. train wreck near Nashville, Tennessee, kills 101
c. coal mine explosion in Dawson, New Mexico, kills 263

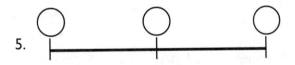

5.

a. earthquake in Japan kills 140,000
b. sinking of the *Andrea Doria* kills 52
c. 236 killed in a train crash in Buenos Aires, Argentina

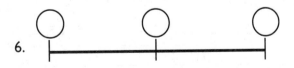

6.

a. explosion of *Challenger* space shuttle kills all aboard
b. sinking of the *Lusitania* kills 1,195
c. 1,200 lives and 2 billion trees lost in Wisconsin forest fire

Answer Key

Page 5: Okay or No Way?

1. Okay. Orville Wright died in 1948; Chuck Yaeger broke the sound barrier in 1947.
2. No way. Edison died in 1931; Roosevelt was elected in 1932.
3. Okay. X-rays were discovered by Roentgen in 1895 and used shortly thereafter; McKinley was assassinated in 1901.
4. Okay. The photocopier was invented in 1938; Truman's inaugural address was 1949.
5. No way. The first Kentucky Derby was run in 1875; Lincoln was shot in 1865.
6. No way. Elvis died in 1977; the first CDs were available in 1982.
7. Okay. The *Andrea Doria* sank in 1956; the aqualung was developed in 1945.

Page 6: Clueless

1. T. Roosevelt: a, k
2. Washington: b, d
3. Hoover: c, o
4. Jefferson: d, h
5. Jackson: e, m
6. Clinton: f, n
7. Lincoln: g, j
8. G.H. Bush: h, i
9. F. Roosevelt: i, l
10. Grant: j, g
11. Kennedy: k, a
12. Reagan: l, e
13. Nixon: m, c
14. Eisenhower: n, b
15. Truman: o, f

Page 7: Herstory

1. Clara Barton
2. Jackie Cochran
3. Dolley Madison
4. Sandra Day O'Connor
5. Geraldine Ferraro
6. Eleanor Roosevelt
7. Annie Oakley (Phoebe Ann Moses)
8. Sacagawea
9. Dorothea Lange
10. Maya Lin
11. Hillary Rodham Clinton
12. Martha Washington

Page 8: What a Discovery!

1. Wright's lights
2. Bell's shells
3. Cousteau's plateaus
4. Howe's cows
5. Nobel's yells
6. Colt's bolts
7. Deere's piers
8. Curie's flurries
9. Ford's awards
10. Schick's bricks
11. Salk's talks
12. Einstein's sunshine
13. Fahrenheit's graphites
14. Freud's employed

Page 9: Name Game

Answers will vary.

Page 10: High and Dry

1. Rocky Mountains
2. Gobi
3. Mount Aconcagua
4. Mount Ararat
5. Himalaya
6. Kalahari
7. Andes
8. Mauna Loa
9. Himalaya
10. Mont Blanc
11. Kilimanjaro
12. Himalaya
13. Mount McKinley
14. Atacama Desert
15. Atlas Mountains
16. Pyrenees
17. Sahara Desert
18. Atacama Desert
19. Sahara Desert
20. Black Hills

Page 11: Battle Plan

1. b, a, c
2. a, b, c
3. a, b, c
4. a, b, c
5. c, a, b
6. a, b, c
7. a, c, b
8. a, b, c
9. c, b, a

Page 12: Think Fast

Answers will vary. For example:

1. Peru, Lima (Peru), Lyon (France)
2. Yellowknife, Red Sea, Blue Nile
3. Antarctica, Europe, Asia
4. Canberra
5. Botswana, Whitehorse
6. Spain, France, Rome
7. New Zealand, Zaïre, Switzerland

Page 13: Who's in the News?

1. Benjamin Franklin
2. Orville Wright
3. John Wilkes Booth
4. Chuck Yeager
5. Charles Lindbergh
6. Neil Armstrong
7. Jonas Salk
8. Audie Murphy
9. Clara Barton
10. Henry Ford
11. Eli Whitney
12. Rosa Parks
13. Norman Schwarzkopf
14. Martin Luther King, Jr.
15. John Brown

Page 14: American Flag Fun

All three flags feature…

1. a bird, Iowa
2. mammals, Pennsylvania
3. the state seal in center, Wyoming
4. one large white star, North Carolina
5. a white background, Rhode Island
6. a tree, Maine
7. the name of the state in all caps, Iowa
8. an eagle, Utah
9. the state's motto, Virginia
10. ships, New York

Page 15: Hide and Seek

Answers will vary; for example:

1. Denver, Denmark
2. Cleveland, Andorra
3. Oregon, Korea
4. Montana, Tanzania
5. Nashville, Kashmir
6. Manhattan, Germany
7. San Francisco, France
8. Sherman Oaks, Chernobyl
9. Washington, Canton
10. Santa Fe, Antarctica

Page 16: Name That State

1. 1803; OH; becomes a state
2. 1958; Colorado Springs, CO; train cadets for Air Force
3. 1832; Lake Itasca, MN; Henry Schoolcraft
4. 1969; TX; Dr. Denton Cooley; first artificial heart transplant at Texas Heart Institute
5. 1936; Black Canyon of Colorado River; created Lake Mead to provide water and power and to control flooding on Colorado River
6. 1945; near Alamogordo, NM; test for use as potential WWII weapon
7. 1963; Canton, OH; honor outstanding pro football players
8. 1872; WY, ID, MT; Yellowstone National Park
9. 1941; Black Hills, SD; Mount Rushmore
10. 1910 (first official one under law signed by Nixon, 1972); Spokane, WA; honor fathers
11. 1921; WV; raise money on sales of goods and services
12. 1882; Appleton, WI; provide electricity
13. 1905; Hershey, PA; Hershey plant

Page 17: Capital Con-VENN-tion

1. Baton Rouge, Carson City, Jefferson City, Little Rock, Oklahoma City
2. Santa Fe
3. Atlanta, Augusta, Madison, Olympia
4. Des Moines, St. Paul
5. none
6. Concord, Jackson, Lansing, Lincoln, Phoenix, Raleigh, Trenton
7. Austin, Bismarck, Boise, Boston, Cheyenne, Denver, Dover, Frankfort, Hartford, Juneau, Nashville, Pierre, Richmond, Salem, Springfield
8. Albany, Annapolis, Charleston, Columbia, Columbus, Harrisburg, Helena, Honolulu, Indianapolis, Montgomery, Montpelier, Providence, Sacramento, Salt Lake City, Tallahassee, Topeka

Page 18: Presidential Rare Pairs

1. Dwight's flights
2. Abe's Babe
3. George's gorge
4. Grover's clovers
5. Taft's rafts
6. Hoover's mover
7. Ford's gourds
8. Grant's pants
9. Teddy's ready
10. James's flames
11. scary Harry
12. Carter's barter
13. Bill's quills
14. Warren's foreign
15. Hayes's maize
16. Polk's yolks
17. Taylor's trailer
18. Ike's trikes
19. Martin's cartons
20. Ronald's McDonald's

Page 19: Flag Trios

Note: Countries added may vary; for example:

1. Tunisia (large circle in center)
2. Australia (Union Jack part of design)
3. Somalia (one star)
4. Kyrgyzstan (solid red background)
5. Indonesia (red and white)
6. Luxembourg (red, white, and blue)
7. Pakistan (star and crescent)
8. Zimbabwe (bird)
9. Italy (three vertical stripes)
10. Kiribati (sun)
11. Vietnam (red and yellow)

Page 20: Women Only

Headlines will vary; for example:

1. 1892; Hillsboro, WV; Author of *The Good Earth* wins 1932 Pulitzer Prize; 1938 Nobel Prize in Literature
2. 1860; Savannah, GA; Georgia Woman Organizes First Girl Scout Patrol in 1912
3. 1844; Allegheny City (now Pittsburgh), PA; Cassatt Wins Acclaim with Impressionist Paintings
4. 1907; Springdale, PA; Marine Biologist Pens *Silent Spring* to Call Attention to Pesticides
5. 1932; San Francisco, CA; American Zoologist Describes Research in *Gorillas in the Mist*
6. 1880; Tuscumbia, AL; Author Chronicles Struggle To Overcome Adversity in Books Translated Into More Than 50 Languages
7. 1860; Washington Co., NY; Folk Artist Holds First One-Artist Show at Age 80
8. 1867; Cochran's Mills, PA; Journalist Circumnavigates Globe in Record 72 Days, 6 Hours, 11 Minutes as Stunt for Newspaper
9. 1913; Tuskegee, AL; Civil Rights Activist Triggers Montgomery Bus Boycott
10. 1897; Atchison, KS; First Female Aviator Crosses Atlantic

Page 21: Where in the World?

1. Poland
2. Pakistan
3. Argentina
4. Germany
5. Portugal
6. Norway
7. Madagascar
8. Nigeria
9. United States
10. Vietnam
11. Thailand
12. Yugoslavia
13. Colombia
14. Netherlands
15. Singapore
16. Monaco
17. Iceland
18. Mongolia
19. Ireland
20. Sweden

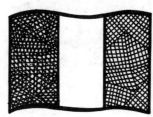

59

Page 22: Presidential Firsts

1. Thomas Jefferson
2. Andrew Jackson
3. Martin Van Buren
4. Andrew Jackson
5. Herbert Hoover
6. Richard Nixon
7. Ulysses S. Grant
8. Rutherford B. Hayes
9. Theodore Roosevelt
10. John F. Kennedy
11. William H. Taft
12. William Henry Harrison
13. Woodrow Wilson
14. Warren G. Harding
15. Franklin D. Roosevelt
16. Lyndon B. Johnson
17. Franklin Pierce
18. Jimmy Carter

Page 23: State of Confusion

Answers will vary; for example:

1. Four-letter words: many, coal, wand, cone, lame, dewy, coin, paid, pail, came
2. Six- or eight-letter words: condor, alarms, marine, demand, Coca-Cola, deride

Page 24: Capital Ideas

1. Salem, OR
2. Tallahassee, FL
3. Springfield, IL
4. Austin, TX
5. Salt Lake City, UT
6. Topeka, KS
7. Trenton, NJ
8. Pierre, SD
9. Helena, MT
10. Indianapolis, IN
11. St. Paul, MN
12. Denver, CO

Page 25: Landmark Occasions

Headlines will vary; for example:

1. 1884 (completed); Washington, DC; Memorial to First President Modeled After Egyptian Obelisk
2. 1753; Philadelphia, PA; Third Version of Bell Finds Home in Independence Hall
3. 1965; St. Louis, MO; Memorial to Thomas Jefferson and Louisiana Purchase Commemorates City's Role as Gateway to the West
4. 1962; Seattle, WA; Space Needle Makes Spectacular Centerpiece for World's Fair
5. 1941; Black Hills, SD; American Leaders Honored with Granite Monument
6. 1884; New York, NY (Liberty Island); Bartholdi Designs Statue to Commemorate First Centennial of American Independence
7. 1922 (dedicated); Washington, DC; 18-Foot Marble Statue by Daniel Chester French Forms Centerpiece of Memorial to Lincoln
8. 1753; Philadelphia, PA; New Statehouse for Pennsylvania Colony Constructed in Georgian Style
9. c. 1722; San Antonio, TX; Texans Defending Alamo Can't Withstand Mexican Army Assault—All Perish
10. 1937; San Francisco, CA; Spectacular Suspension Bridge Spans Entrance to San Francisco Bay

Page 26: Keyography

Answers will vary. Accept any words that meet the given criteria.

Page 27: Presidential Ad-VENN-tures

1. McKinley, Taft, Harding, Kennedy, Carter
2. Wilson, F. Roosevelt, Reagan
3. Eisenhower, Clinton
4. George H.W. Bush
5. T. Roosevelt, Coolidge
6. L. Johnson, Nixon, Truman
7. Ford
8. Hoover

Page 28: Time Flies!

1. a, b, c
2. c, b, a
3. c, b, a
4. c, b, a
5. b, c, a
6. b, c, a
7. b, a, c
8. a, c, b
9. a, b, c

Page 29: Colorful Geography

1. Red Sea
2. Whitehorse
3. Yellowstone
4. Blue Ridge Mtns.
5. Red River
6. Greenland
7. Black Sea
8. Greenwich, Engl.
9. Yellowknife
10. Black Hills
11. Baton Rouge
12. Yellow River
13. Green Bay
14. White Sands, NM
15. Black Forest
16. Yellow Sea
17. Green Mountains
18. White Mountains

Page 30: Which War?

1. i
2. i
3. h
4. g
5. d
6. c
7. h
8. g
9. d
10. a
11. b
12. b
13. g
14. d
15. d
16. a
17. d
18. a
19. e
20. e
21. j
22. f
23. g
24. g
25. f
26. f
27. e
28. c
29. i
30. a
31. a
32. g
33. a
34. i
35. i
36. a
37. h
38. a
39. a
40. j
41. b
42. d
43. a
44. f
45. e
46. b
47. d
48. f
49. d
50. e

Page 31: It's a Date!

1. 1914
2. 1991
3. 1971
4. 1986
5. 1928
6. 1929
7. 1849
8. 1844
9. 1859
10. 1896
11. 1886
12. 1863
13. 1927
14. 1937
15. 1920

Page 32: Alien Invasion

1. Brazil
2. Thailand
3. Spain
4. Turkey
5. New Zealand
6. Sudan
7. Saudi Arabia
8. India
9. Mexico

Page 33: Keypad Characters

1. George
2. Bonaparte
3. Wright
4. Scott
5. Milhous
6. Hillary
7. Fleming
8. Shepard

Page 34: I Don't Think So!

1. Okay: Indy 500 first run in 1911; Ford died 1947
2. I don't think so: Post-It© Notes invented 1974; Einstein died 1955
3. I don't think so: Polartec introduced 1991; Hillary climbed Everest 1953
4. Okay: Lincoln shot 1865; transcontinental telegraph completed 1861
5. I don't think so: Grant elected 1868; microphone invented 1876
6. Okay: First shuttle launched 1981; first video game, Pong, 1972
7. I don't think so: Connors's first U.S. Open win 1974; oversized racquet introduced 1976

61

Page 35: It's a Wonder!

1. Lighthouse of Alexandria
2. Colossus of Rhodes
3. Mausoleum at Halicarnassus
4. Temple of Artemis at Ephesus
5. Pyramids of Egypt at Giza
6. Statue of Zeus
7. Colossus of Rhodes
8. Hanging Gardens of Babylon
9. Colossus of Rhodes
10. Colossus of Rhodes, Lighthouse of Alexandria, Mausoleum at Halicarnassus
11. Hanging Gardens of Babylon
12. Lighthouse of Alexandria
13. Mausoleum at Halicarnassus
14. Temple of Artemis at Ephesus
15. Mausoleum at Halicarnassus
16. Pyramids of Egypt at Giza
17. Lighthouse of Alexandria
18. Statue of Zeus

Page 36: Monumental Discoveries

1. Terra-cotta army buried in military formation near tomb of Chinese emperor Shi Huangdi, near Xi'an
2. Olmec carved basalt heads
3. Parthenon
4. Easter Island statues
5. Sphinx
6. Colossus of Rhodes
7. Colosseum
8. Stonehenge
9. Trajan's Column
10. Macchu Picchu

Page 37: Let's Get Civilized

Note: Order of answers may vary.

1. Ancient Egypt: ankh, cat mummies, hieroglyphics, papyrus boats, Osiris, pharaohs, potter's wheel, Rosetta stone, senet, Sphinx, Thebes
2. Ancient Greece: Acropolis, catapult, drachma, Homer, Icarus, Ionic Order, Lion Gate, Olympics, Socrates, Sparta, triremes, Trojan War
3. Ancient Rome: aqueduct, arched bridges, Colosseum, fasces, Forum, gladiators, legionnaire, Hadrian's Wall, Pompeii, public baths, senate, signs of the zodiac, toga

Page 38: Architectural Ad-VENN-tures

1. Colosseum, Leaning Tower of Pisa, Taj Mahal
2. Statue of Liberty, U.S. Capitol, White House
3. Lincoln Memorial
4. Eiffel Tower
5. Washington Monument
6. Gateway Arch, Space Needle, Sears Tower
7. Petronas Towers
8. Sydney Opera House

Page 39: Presidential Newsmakers

1. Jimmy Carter
2. William Howard Taft
3. Theodore Roosevelt
4. George H.W. Bush
5. Calvin Coolidge
6. Dwight Eisenhower and Richard Nixon
7. James Garfield
8. Thomas Jefferson, John Adams
9. Lyndon Johnson
10. Bill Clinton
11. Grover Cleveland
12. Benjamin Harrison
13. Millard Fillmore
14. Woodrow Wilson
15. Harry Truman

Page 40: Capital Anagrams

1. Sacramento
2. Montpelier
3. Carson City
4. Tallahassee
5. Springfield
6. Indianapolis
7. Providence
8. Jefferson City
9. Olympia
10. Harrisburg
11. Des Moines
12. Charleston
13. Salt Lake City
14. Bismarck
15. Santa Fe
16. Topeka
17. Oklahoma City
18. Annapolis
19. Baton Rouge
20. Montgomery

Page 41: D.C. Landmarks

1. Smithsonian Air and Space Museum
2. National Archives
3. Arlington National Cemetery
4. Vietnam Veterans Memorial
5. Washington Monument
6. Jefferson Memorial
7. Ford's Theatre
8. U.S. Capitol
9. Iwo Jima Statue
10. Bureau of Engraving and Printing

Page 42: Who Said So?

1. Nathan Hale
2. Patrick Henry
3. Benjamin Franklin
4. John F. Kennedy
5. Martin Luther King, Jr.
6. Neil Armstrong
7. Franklin D. Roosevelt
8. Francis Scott Key
9. Abraham Lincoln
10. Thomas Jefferson

Page 43: A Rainbow of Facts

1. Blackfeet
2. White House
3. silversmith
4. Red Cross
5. Purple Heart
6. gold rush
7. John Brown
8. Yellowhammer
9. bluebonnet
10. Golden Gate Bridge
11. Green Mountain boys
12. Cincinnati Red Stockings
13. Blackbeard
14. Redcoats
15. greenhouse effect
16. Black History Month
17. Golden State
18. blue spruce

Page 44: More Keyography

Answers will vary. Accept any answers that meet the given criteria.

Page 45: That's Silly!

Answers will vary. Accept any answers that meet the given criteria.

Page 46: Historic Headlines

1. 1733; Benjamin Franklin publishes the first of his annual almanacs full of advice, proverbs, poems, and weather predictions.
2. 1804–1806; Lewis and Clark explore the wilderness of the Louisiana Purchase from St. Louis to the Pacific.
3. 1770; Boston Massacre was the killing of Crispus Attucks and several other colonists by British soldiers and was one of the events that led to the Revolutionary War.
4. 1775; Daniel Boone and a party of frontiersmen began to cut a trail through the Cumberland Mountains from Tennessee to what is now Kentucky.
5. 1847; Brigham Young led Mormons to settle in the Great Salt Lake valley.
6. 1860; Pony Express relay riders take mail from St. Joseph, MO, to Sacramento, CA, (1,966 miles) in 10 days.
7. 1590; John White's supply ship arrived at Roanoke Island off the coast of present-day North Carolina to find that the entire colony had been abandoned.
8. 1620; Pilgrims signed the Mayflower Compact to set up a government in the Plymouth Colony.
9. 1814; Francis Scott Key pens the poem "The Star-Spangled Banner," which would become the national anthem of the United States.
10. 1869; Transcontinental Railroad was completed in Utah when the Central Pacific Railroad (coming east from Sacramento) and the Union Pacific Railroad (coming west from Omaha) finally met.
11. 1836; Texan defenders of the Alamo in San Antonio were all killed when attacked by the Mexican army.
12. 1865; General Robert E. Lee surrendered the Confederate troops to Ulysses S. Grant at Appomattox Courthouse in rural Virginia.
13. 1825; the Erie Canal was completed, joining the Great Lakes to the Atlantic.

Page 47: Next-Door Neighbors

Answers will vary; for example:

1. Des Moines, Denver, Ghent, Detroit
2. Philadelphia, Adelaide, Copenhagen
3. Ghana, Denmark, Norway, Tunisia
4. Afghanistan, Costa Rica
5. Denali, Pocono Mountains
6. North Sea; Strait of Magellan

Page 48: More Fun with Place Names

Answers will vary.

Page 49: Baseball Greats Rare Pairs

1. Mark's sparks
2. Mickey's tricky
3. Ted's breads
4. Joe's woes
5. Ty's surprise
6. Yogi's hoagies
7. Wade's spades
8. Pete's feats
9. Stan's plans
10. Ruth's truths
11. Ken's hens
12. Barry's canaries
13. Willie's chilis
14. Steve's sleeves
15. Cal's pals
16. Sammy's whammies
17. Roy's noise
18. Hank's planks
19. Sandy's candies
20. Ford's awards

Page 50: Liquid Logic

1. Lake Tanganyika
2. Lake Titicaca
3. Lake Nipigon, Reindeer Lake, Lake Winnipeg
4. Lake Victoria
5. Weddell Sea
6. Caribbean Sea, Hudson Bay, Bering Sea
7. Baltic Sea, Bay of Bengal, Caspian Sea, Red Sea
8. Lake Rudolph, Aral Sea

Page 51: River Riddles

1. Rio Grande
2. Thames
3. Zambezi
4. Volga
5. Missouri
6. Potomac
7. Ganges
8. Danube
9. Jordan
10. Delaware
11. Mackenzie
12. Niagara
13. Nile
14. St. Lawrence
15. Seine

Page 52: That's Not Natural!

1. Leaning Tower of Pisa; Pisa, Italy
2. Taj Mahal; Agra, India
3. Big Ben; London, England
4. Kremlin; Moscow, Russia
5. Trans-Alaska Pipeline; Alaska
6. Christ the Redeemer; Rio de Janeiro, Brazil
7. Channel Tunnel (Chunnel); Folkstone, England, to Coquelles (near Calais), France
8. Sydney Opera House; Sydney, Australia
9. Palace of Versailles; Versailles, France
10. Grand Canal; China
11. Alhambra; Spain
12. Mt. Vernon; Virginia

Page 53: Decade Dilemma

Note: Order of letters may vary

1. 1940s: d, f, g, k, m, p
2. 1950s: a, e, i, j, l, q, t, u
3. 1960s: b, c, h, n, o, r, s

Page 54: Early Americans

1. b	9. a,c,e	17. b	25. a
2. d	10. c	18. a	26. b
3. a,c	11. b	19. c	27. c
4. d	12. a	20. a	28. d
5. b	13. d	21. d	29. b
6. e	14. d	22. a	30. c
7. d	15. b	23. c	31. a
8. b	16. d	24. e	32. a,c,e

Page 55: Continental Geography

1. Africa: 2, 5, 7, 10, 32, 34, 40
2. Asia: 3, 8, 23, 26, 30, 31, 38, 45, 47
3. Australia: 1, 6, 11, 15, 20, 29, 36, 43, 48
4. Europe: 13, 17, 19, 28, 33, 39, 41, 42
5. North America: 4, 9, 16, 22, 24, 27, 37, 46
6. South America: 12, 14, 18, 21, 25, 35, 44

Page 56: What a Disaster!

1. a, c, b
2. b, c, a
3. a, b, c
4. c, b, a
5. a, b, c
6. c, b, a